royal ulster academy of arts

124TH ANNUAL EXHIBITION

16TH SEPTEMBER - 9TH OCTOBER 2005

ULSTER MUSEUM BELFAST

The Academy wishes to thank the following
organisations and companies for their support:

Mills Selig Solicitors

The Mooney Hotel Group

Emer Gallery

The Irish News Ltd.

Ulster Arts Club

Mullan Gallery

Blackstaff Press

Gallery 148, Holywood, Co. Down

Coloured Rain

Nicholson & Bass Ltd

Ross's Auctioneers

Delivery Services, Belfast

Conor's Bistro Cafe

Carol Graham SEAWAY

Welcome to the 124th RUA Annual Exhibition the most popular and successful showcase of contemporary art in the Province. As the first woman President in nearly 30 years, I am honoured to be following in the footsteps of such notables as Sir John Lavery, Rosamund Praeger and William Conor.

I am delighted to announce that Pauline Bewick RHA has accepted our invitation to be this year's Awards Adjudicator, and I am particularly pleased that our Guest Exhibitor this year is Hughie O'Donoghue.

New initiatives for Academy Members in 2006 include exhibition opportunities in Hillsborough and Boyle, Co. Roscommon, whilst the Permanent RUA Collection will travel to the Glebe Gallery in Donegal.

I have taken office at a time of great change in the Academy: in personnel terms, we have a new Vice-President, Honorary Secretary, Treasurer and introduced the post of Exhibition Administrator.

Many thanks to Joe McWilliams and his Vice-President John Breakey for all their hard work on behalf of the Academy. Among the initiatives of Joe's term were the introduction of this splendid Catalogue format, this year designed by Colin Davidson, and the widening of the Academy's portfolio of art collectors.

Appreciation is also due to Kay McKelvey, for carrying the myriad burdens of RUA Hon. Secretary so effectively for three years.

Ken Kennedy of the Ulster Bank, the Academy's Treasurer for the last ten years, has been a resourceful and loyal contributor to the RUA. We have greatly benefited from his specialist advice and expertise.

R. T. Killen is my current Vice President. Bob has worked steadily on behalf of the Academy, and provided wise counsel behind the scenes for some years now, but I'm not letting him off just yet!

It gives me great pleasure to welcome our new appointees:

Our new Hon. Secretary is Amanda Croft. Amanda will be well known to many as an established and much respected figure in the local arts scene. Her extensive experience as lecturer, curator and advisor will be of great value to the Academy. I already feel the benefit of her calm professionalism.

Barbara Killen is our eminently qualified new Treasurer, whose skills and enthusiasm are most welcome.

Susan Abraham took up the post of Exhibition Administrator last year. The smooth running of this year's exhibition is the result of her organisational skills and the Academy greatly values her professional expertise.

This year I introduced a two day selection process and we are grateful to selectors Bernard Jaffa, Anne Stewart and Eileen Black who gave generously of their time and experience, as well as hard-working members of the Academy.

I would like to record our thanks to our Exhibition partner the Ulster Museum and their staff for all their help and expertise. Gratitude is also due to our many sponsors, established and new, for their generous contributions. This year we are introducing an invitation morning for sponsors, prize winners, press and corporate collection purchasers, which we hope will create interesting and beneficial encounters!

However, the most formidable challenge which the Academy is facing is the loss, from 2006 – 2008, of its annual Exhibition space, due to the impending closure of the Ulster Museum for major building renovations. We have enjoyed a unique and mutually successful partnership with the Museum for much of the last two decades.

The Annual Exhibition attracts 500-600 entries from artists throughout Ireland and beyond, has a footfall average of 14,000 visitors and extensive sales of works.

At stake is one of the most important events in the Northern Ireland arts calendar for artists, the public, the general arts community and the Academy itself. Its potential suspension would be a major loss to these groups and especially to the many thousands of art lovers who visit the Exhibition.

In tandem with the RUA Council and others, I am fully committed to finding a constructive solution to these challenges. We continue to explore creative options, and we look forward, not only to another successful Exhibition in 2005, but to the 125th RUA Annual Exhibition in a new venue next year!

Carol Graham
President
Royal Ulster Academy of Arts
September 2005

royal ulster academy of arts

Patron
The Duke of Abercorn

President
Carol Graham*

Vice President
Bob Killen*

Hon. Secretary
Amanda Croft

Hon. Treasurer
Barbara Killen

Exhibition Administrator
Susan Abraham

Sophie Aghajanian
James Allen*
Brian Ballard
Basil Blackshaw
Robert Bottom*
John Breakey
Richard J Croft
Rita Duffy
Jean Duncan
T P Flanagan
Graham Gingles*
Carol Graham*
Helen Kerr
Robert T Killen*
Elizabeth McEwen
James McIntyre
Catherine McWilliams
Joseph McWilliams
Cecil F Maguire
Jack Pakenham
Neil Shawcross
Mark Shields
Bob Sloan
Victor Sloan
Norman Smyth

Barbara Allen
Anne M Anderson
Margaret Arthur*
Betty Brown
Beatrice Chapleo
Joy Clements
Ivor Coburn
Colin Davidson*
Chris Dearden
Daniel Dowling
Denise Ferran
Julian Friers*
Michael Ginnett
William Hanna
Les Jones
Phyllis Leopold
Robert Linton
James MacKeever
James Manley
Sheila McClean
Hector McDonnell
Colin McGookin
Rosie McGurran
Gordon McKnight
Simon McWilliams
Joanna Mules
Marcus Patton
Robert Sellar
Mavis Thomson
Veronica Wallis
Paul Walls
Ross Wilson

* Council Members

HONORARY ACADEMICIANS

Lydia de Burgh
Deborah Brown
R Taylor Carson
David Evans
Brian Ferran
Solly Lipsitz
Gladys Maccabe
John McMillan
Dennis Osborne
Raymond Piper
Harry Reid
James Scott
Desmond Turner
John Turner

HONORARY MEMBERS

The President, The Royal Academy
The President, The Royal Scottish Academy
The President, The Royal Hibernian Academy
The President, The Royal Society of Ulster Architects
The President, The Ulster Arts Club
The President, The Ulster Society of Women Artists
The President, The Ulster Watercolour Society
The President, The Arts Society of Ulster
The Chairman, Arts Council of Northern Ireland
The Director, The National Gallery Ireland
Martyn Anglesea, Keeper of Fine Art Ulster Museum
Elizabeth McCrum, Acting Head of Fine and Applied Art Ulster Museum
Dr Brian Kennedy
Andrew Crockart
Doreen Crockart
Peter Ford
Dr R B Henderson

HONORARY ASSOCIATES

Jack Crabtree
Professor Peter Fawcett

ACADEMICIANS SUPPLEMENTAL

The Keeper of Art, Ulster Museum
The Exhibitions Officer, Arts Council of Northern Ireland
The Registrar, Royal Ulster Academy

**RUA PERPETUAL GOLD MEDAL
AND THE COLOURED RAIN PRIZE**
£600
The RUA Perpetual Gold Medal,
originally presented by the late Wilfred J.
Haughton, PPRUA, is awarded for the
best work by a member of the Academic
Body of the Royal Ulster Academy.

Colin Davidson

**RUA PERPETUAL SILVER MEDAL
AND GALLERY 148 PRIZE** *£300*
The RUA Perpetual Silver Medal is
awarded for the most outstanding work by
an artist who is not a member of the
Academic body of the RUA.

Sam Mateer

**RUA PRESIDENT'S PRIZE
AND LANESIDE GALLERY PRIZE** *£300*
For the best work by a student.

Anne McKeown

BLACKSTAFF PRESS PRIZE *£500*
For a still life.

Naomi Fitzpatrick

CONOR PRIZE *£800*
The Mooney Hotel Group sponsors this
prize and the Academy awards a bronze
medal (donated by James Scott) to
perpetuate the memory of William Conor,
for an outstanding pictorial work in any
medium in which the main focus of
interest is a figure or figures.

Carol Graham

EMER GALLERY PRIZE *£750*
For the best self-portrait in any medium.

Michael Bell

IRISH NEWS PRIZE *£500*
For a work in any medium depicting
the theme 'Ireland Today'

Jack Pakenham

MILLS SELIG PRIZE *£1,000*
For an outstanding painting by a
young artist (age limit 35 years)

Stephen Forbes

MULLAN GALLERY PRIZE *£500*
For the best bronze sculpture.

Bob Sloan

NICHOLSON & BASS AWARD *£300*
For the best print.

Margaret Arthur

PAUL HENRY LANDSCAPE PRIZE
£500
Clement McAleer

ROSS'S WATERCOLOUR PRIZE *£300*

Chris Dearden

ULSTER ARTS CLUB PRIZE *£500*
For the best abstract work.

Angela Hackett

**ANNA CHEYNE CERAMIC
SCULPTURE PRIZE**
(age limit 35 years) *£400*

Majella McManus

Pauline Bewick   WOMAN FISHING AT LIKEEN

CATALOGUE OF WORKS

ACADEMICIANS

Sophie Aghajanian
1. GLASS IMAGE *Oil on canvas 51 x 61 cm £1,650*
2. VANISHING EDGE *Oil on canvas 51 x 61 cm £1,650*

James Allen
3. FIGURES IN AN OLD LANDSCAPE *Oil on board 26 x 30 cm £875*
4. CLOUD BREAK *Oil on canvas 25 x 30 cm £750*

Brian Ballard
5. TEAPOT AND PAINTS *Oil on canvas 61 x 46 cm £5,600*
6. LUCY ON PURPLE *Oil on canvas 46 x 61 cm £5,600*

Basil Blackshaw
7. SEATED NUDE *Oil and pencil on paper 61 x 45.7 cm N.F.S.*

Robert D. Bottom
8. TOWARDS FAIR HEAD, BALLYCASTLE, CO. ANTRIM (1) *Oil 61 x 66 cm £1,850*
9. TOWARDS FAIR HEAD, BALLYCASTLE, CO. ANTRIM (2) *Oil 41 x 51 cm £1,000*

John Breakey
10. TWO STONES ON A BEACH FULL OF STONES *Oil 122 x 152 cm £3,500*
11. THE TASTE OF THE SEA IS GREEN *Watercolour 77 x 97 cm £850*

Richard J Croft
12. CHERRIES *Oil 101 x 230 cm £5,750*
13. APPLES *Oil 101 x 101 cm £3,750*

Jean Duncan
14. NOVEMBER HILLSIDE, KERRY *Oil on canvas 65 x 74 cm £1,250*
15. INLET, BOLUS HEAD *Oil on canvas 50 x 55 cm £850*

T. P. Flanagan
16. IN THE BLACK GAP, CO. DONEGAL *Oil on canvas 63.5 x 76.2 cm £7,000*
17. WEIR LISMORE *Oil on canvas 101.6 x 76.2 cm £11,500*

Graham Gingles
18. NUDE WITH PALM TREE *Oil on canvas 53 x 43 cm £850*

Carol Graham
19. SEAWAY *Oil on canvas 97 x 102 cm £5,200*
20. PORTRAIT OF LORD ALDERDICE *Oil on canvas 170 x 120 cm N.F.S.*

Helen Kerr
21. LAND BELOW THE WIND (TRYPTCH) *Batik/stitch 80 x 187 cm £2,500*
22. FLYING NORTH *Batik/stitch 90 x 75 cm £2,000*

R.T. Killen
23. RELIGIOUS GATHERING, GONDAR, ETHIOPIA *Oil 28 x 37 cm £750*
24. TREES – LOUGH CONN *Oil 28 x 37 cm £600*

Cecil Maguire
25. BALLINASLOE FAIR *Oil 75 x 60 cm £9,000*
26. ST. GEORGES MARKET BELFAST *Oil 75 x 60 cm £9,000*

Hughie O'Donoghue EXODUS

Elizabeth McEwen	27.	TULIPS *Watercolour 40 x 61 cm £350*
	28.	DAISIES AND DELFT *Watercolour 47 x 4 cm £400*
Catherine McWilliams	29.	RED TREES; CAVE HILL *Oil on canvas 56 x 67 cm £2,200*
	30.	INSIDE THE BLACK MOUNTAIN *Acrylic on paper 49 x 62 cm £1,300*
Joseph McWilliams	31.	BELFAST FROM THE CAVEHILL *Oil on canvas 80 x 120 cm £4,500*
	32.	ORANGE UMBRELLA *Oil on handmade paper 28 x 37 cm £2,000*
Jack Pakenham	33.	CLOWN'S HOLIDAY DILEMMA I *Acrylic on canvas 103 x 102 cm £2,500*
	34.	CLOWN'S HOLIDAY DILEMMA II *Acrylic on canvas 103 x 102 cm £2,500*
Neil Shawcross	35.	PORTRAIT OF TED HICKEY *Oil on canvas 207 x 100 cm N.F.S.*
	36.	PORTRAIT OF GRAHAM GINGLES *Oil on canvas 207 x 100 cm N.F.S*
Bob Sloan	37.	HITCHCOCKS'S CHAIR *Ed. 1/8 Bronze 29 x 14 x 21 cm £2,000*
	38.	LONG TALL SALLY *Ed 1/8 Bronze 26 x 10 x 8 cm £1,000*
Victor Sloan	39.	GROUND II *Etching with watercolours 47 x30 cm £790*
	40.	GROUND III *Etching with watercolours 47 x 30 cm £790*
Norman Smyth	41.	KINNAGOE BAY CO. DONEGAL *Oil 46 x 56 cm £2,750*
	42.	DRYING TURF *Oil 25 x 35 cm £1,100*

A S S O C I A T E   A C A D E M I C I A N S

Barbara Allen	43.	THE DRAWING OFFICES OF HARLAND & WOLFF *Watercolour 80 x 56 cm £750*
Anne M. Anderson	44.	SEPTEMBER DUSK *Viscosity etching 18.5 x 19 cm £160 £98 u/f*
	45.	MAY MORNING *Viscosity etching 18.5 x 19 cm £160 £98 u/f*
Margaret Arthur	46.	MASKED I *Mixed media monoprint 69 x 82 cm £285*
	47.	IRIS *Mixed media monoprint 74 x 80 cm £320*
Betty Brown	48.	LIKE A DOG *Assemblage sculpture mixed media 120 x 80 x 40 cm £500*
Beatrice Chapleo	49.	WAY OF LIFE *Acrylic 60 x 90 cm £800*
	50.	DOWN AT THE DOCKS *Oil 20 x 35 cm £350*
Joy Clements	51.	INNER DOORWAY *Oil 50 x 42 cm £800*
	52.	CLAY POT WITH FRUIT *Pastel 42 x 44 cm £500*
Ivor B. Coburn	53.	HELENIUM *Watercolour 104.2 x 76.2 cm £2,500*
	54.	IRISES *Watercolour 104.2 x 76.2 cm £2,500*
Colin Davidson	55.	BELFAST LANDSCAPE: TOWARDS CAVEHILL FROM BEDFORD HOUSE *Oil 76 x 102 cm £5,500*
	56.	BELFAST LANDSCAPE: SOUTH FROM RIVER HOUSE *Lithograph 30 x 39 cm £350 f £250 uf*
Chris Dearden	57.	CHICKEN RUN *Watercolour 66.7 x 66.3 cm £650*
	58.	CHICKEN SHACK *Watercolour 55.5 x 77.8 cm £650*

R. T. Killen TREES – LOUGH CONN

Daniel Dowling	59.	MONDAY MORNING AT FORT WILLIAM *Oil on canvas 70 x 100 cm £2,250*
	60.	WALKING THE DOG AT CHICHESTER *Oil on canvas 70 x 100 cm £2,250*
Denise Ferran	61.	CLOUDS OVER NEWCASTLE BEACH *Acrylic on canvas 76 x 102 cm £1,350*
	62.	LOWER LOUGH ERNE FROM NAVAR FOREST *Acrylic on canvas 76 x 102 cm £1,350*
Julian Friers	63.	JOE KENNEDY *Oil on canvas 61 x 45 cm N.F.S*
	64.	KING FISHER *Oil on panel 23 x 33 cm £1,500*
M.C. Ginnett	65.	YOUTH *Oil 62 x 52 cm £850*
	66.	PORTRAIT OF JOHN O'REGAN *Oil 77 x 51 cm £650*
Les Jones	67.	THE WHITE HOUSE, SANDSEND, N. YORKS. *Watercolour 28 x 31 cm £950*
	68.	GIRL IN WHITE TOP, CASTLEWARD, CO. DOWN *Watercolour 25 x 29 cm £800*
James MacKeever	69.	WAITING *Terracotta 50 cm £600*
	70.	BEGINNING *Terracotta 45 cm £450*
Jim Manley	71.	CUCKOO WRASSE TRALEE BAY *Watercolour/acrylic 45 x 60 cm £950*
	72.	RED CABBAGE COMBER RIVER *Watercolour/acrylic 45 x 60 cm £950*
Sheila McClean	73.	PULSE OF THE BOG *Oil on board 61 x 61 cm £1,200*
	74.	AMID THE HEATHER HUMMOCKS *Oil on plywood 61 x 71.1 cm £1,350*
Colin McGookin	75.	SHORE *Acrylic on linen 45 x 33 cm £400*
	76.	TUNE *Acrylic on linen 43 x 31 cm £400*
Rosie McGurran	77.	ISLAND BRIDE *Charcoal/paper 100 x 86 cm £1,500*
	78.	GUARDIANS *Charcoal/paper 100 x 93 cm £1,500*
Gordon McKnight	79.	STILL WATERS RUN DEEP IN DONEGAL *Watercolour 71 x 60 cm £1,100*
	80.	SPOTLIGHT ON MOUNT STEWART *Watercolour 60 x 80 cm £1,200*
Simon McWilliams	81.	TRAFFIC LIGHTS I *Oil on canvas 178 x 188 £7,500*
	82.	PALM HOUSE, RAINING *Oil on canvas 124 x 145 £5,200*
Joanna Mules	83.	THREE WISHES *Pastel 450 x 600 cm £350*
	84.	RENAISSANCE *Pastel 1200 x 900 cm N.F.S.*
Marcus Patton	85.	SONGS MY MOTHER TAUGHT ME *Mixed media 600 x 450 cm N.F.S.*
	86.	MY LOVELY BANK *Silkscreen print 600 x 450 cm £250*
Mavis Thompson	87.	SELF PORTRAIT – TUNISIAN THOUGHTS *Driftwood construction mixed media and indian ink 42 x 47 x 12 cm N.F.S.*
	88.	COLOURED THOUGHTS ON A SLIGO BUS TRIP WITH POEM *Driftwood construction oil 32 x 39 x 12 cm £1,500*
Veronica J. Wallis	89.	MUCKISH/THE SLEEPING/ PIG *(Monoprint) 30 x 40 cm £250*
	90.	MUCKISH DAWN *Oil on paper (monoprint) 30 x 40 cm £250*
Paul Walls	91.	THERE'S NO PLACE LIKE HOME *Oil 51 x 61 cm £1,875*
	92.	THERE'S NO PLACE LIKE HOME EXPRESSION *Oil 31.5 x 40.6 cm £1,100*
Ross Wilson	93.	LEPUS RHEE *Mixed media 25 x 30 cm £1,450*

Simon McWilliams PALM HOUSE, RAINING

HONORARY ACADEMICIANS

Lydia de Burgh
94. INDIAN GIRL, NEAR AGRA, 1979 *Watercolour   58 x 60 cm   £395*
95. THE WICKLOW GAP, 2004 *Watercolour   65 x 51 cm   £480*

Brian Ferran
96. INIS TRA ULAI I *Acrylic on canvas   76 x 76 cm   £2,800*
97. INIS TRA ULAI II *Acrylic on canvas   61 x 61 cm   £2,400*

Dennis H. Osborne
98. COMPOSITION RED GREEN & BLACK *Acrylic   76 x 76 cm   £1,500*
99. COMPOSITION *Acrylic   39 x 40 cm   £1,000*

Raymond Piper
100. STUDY OF A MALAYSIAN GIRL *Oil   33 x 27 cm   N.F.S.*

Harry Reid
101. HEADLAND AND STRAND, NEWPORT BAY *Acrylic   120 x 80 cm   £2,000*
102. UNTITLED ABSTRACT *Acrylic   41 x 41 cm   £ 800*

James Scott
103. GALWAY HILLS *Oil   41 x 51 cm   £500*
104. LILAC *Oil   41 x 41 cm   £500*

Desmond Turner
105. ROCK POOLS DOOAGH ACHILL WITH SLIEVEMORE *Oil   61 x 95 cm   £6,750*

SELECTED ARTISTS

Henrietta Alexander
106. FUN *Etching   50 x 55 cm   £168   £130 u/f*

Neisha Allen
107. THE RED SHOE *Oil on board   60 x 80 cm   £1,275*

Marion Anderson
108. MOORISH PALACE, GRANADA I *Etching   37 x 33 cm   £100   £65 u/f (13 Avail)*

Michael Ashur
109. NOVA AQUILAE *Acrylic on canvas   122 x 122 cm   £7,500*

Corrina Askin
110. THE MAGPIE & THE SILVER BRACELETS *Screen print   85 x 65 cm   £350*

Deborah Baillie
111. FILE *Sculpture (perspex and plastic)   26 x 41 x 25.5 cm   £200*

Liz Baird
112. AUTUMN *Monoprint   41.5 x 43 cm   £100*

Lisa Ballard
113. NORTH SHORE *Oil on canvas   80 x 60 cm   £1,500*

Tristan Barry
114. GRANDPA'S KNIVES *Oil on canvas   17.5 x 17.5 cm   £230*

Angeline Beattie
115. CLOUDED SURFACE *Acrylic on canvas   61 x 61 cm   £450*

Michael Bell
116. WALLACE HUEY *Oil on canvas   45 x 35 cm   £1,200*
117. ANDREW DALY *Oil on canvas   48 x 45 cm   £1,500*

Gregor Pozzo Berenger
118. A CROSS FOR DORA MAAR *Watercolour/pastel   67 x 53 cm   £350*

Natalia Black
119. PORTAFERRY *Oil on canvas   25 x 30 cm   £575*
120. KEARNEY *Oil on canvas   20 x 27 cm   £525*

Jean Duncan INLET, BOLUS HEAD

Christopher Boyle	121.	BOMB ATTACK WITH POPPY ANDERSONSTOWN BARRACKS *Photograph 30.3 x 45.5 cm £100*
	122.	MACHINE GUN ANDERSONSTOWN BARRACKS FALLS ROAD VIEW *Photograph 30.3 x 45.5 cm £100*
Esther Brimage	123.	WOMAN SITTING *Etching 50.5 x 27 cm £250*
	124.	WHITE CAT *Etching 60.5 x 40.5 cm £275*
John C. Brobbel	125.	CHILDREN'S SHOE – LASTS *Oil 25 x 30 cm £1,500*
Cheryl Brown	126.	MATADOR I *Bronze 40 x 15 x 8 cm £950*
	127.	SUNBIRD I *Bronze 30 x 10 x 4 cm £900*
Mary Burke	128.	SUBURBAN DIAGONALS *Oil pastel on board 106 x 84 cm £1,500*
Ronnie Burton	129.	SUPRALIMINAL *Oil on canvas 92 x 112 cm £800*
Maureen Bushe	130.	JOINT EFFORT *Marble and Kilkenny limestone 19 x 19 x 24 cm £700*
Stuart Cairns	131.	FLOWER FALL *Stainless steel, wire, silver, gold leaf/gold 45 x 30 x 30 cm £750*
Rachael Campbell-Palmer	132.	UNTITLED DRESS *Latex based mixed media 240 x 145 x 105 cm £1,200*
Vernon Carter	133.	SELF-PORTRAIT *Chalk and paint 77 x 53 cm N.F.S*
Comhghall Casey	134.	TOY GUN *Oil on linen 38 x 51 cm £1,600*
Graham Catney	135.	TITANTIC *Lithograph 76.5 x 50 cm £ 485*
Gerry Coe	136.	NO: 5 *Giclee print ltd ed (15) 86 x 65 cm £295 £250 u/f*
John Connery	137.	THE BACK LANE *Oil on canvas 75 x 100 cm £1,600*
Simon Cook	138.	NEW BEGINNINGS *Oil 78 x 1003 cm £2,200*
Colin M. Corkey	139.	THE ISLAND IS SILENT *Wood, sand and acrylic 98 x 82 cm £1,800*
Terence Coyle	140.	SELF-PORTRAIT *Oil on canvas 38 x 31 cm £1,100*
	141.	BEACH DONEGAL *Oil on canvas 61 x 76 cm £1,100*
Alan Daly	142.	THREE SHRIMP *Oil on canvas 12 x 17.5 cm £400*
Fionnuala D'Arcy	143.	LANDSCAPE WITH TREES *Oil on board 35 x 50 cm £450*
Colin Davis	144.	BLUE STAG *Inked lithographic aluminium plates 89 x 132 cm £1,795*
Gerry Devlin	145.	UNDERCURRENT *Oil on canvas 108 x 100 cm £1,800*
Aaron Dickson	146.	SEPTEMBER 12th *Photograph 51 x 38.5cm £200*
Rachel Dickson	147.	THE ART OF SHOWING OFF *Paper 30 x 30 cm £250*
	148.	NUMBER 50 *Paper 30 x 30 cm £250*
Stephen Dillon	149.	UNTITLED 1 *Ceramic 90 cm £400*
	150.	UNTITLED 2 *Ceramic 90 cm £400*

Michael Bell WALLACE HUEY

Frances M. Donnan	151.	THE CENTURION *Ceramic (Raku)* 26 x 19 x 12 cm £290	
Cian Donnelly	152.	SLICE PAINTING IN PRUSSIAN BLUE *Oil* 30 x 30 x 10 cm £1,500	
Tony Donnelly	153.	LANDSCAPE WITH BUSYBODIES *Digital print* 99 x 81 cm £350	
Doreen Dunne	154.	THE BOY, ARTHUR *Bronze on limestone base* 23 x 14 x 11 cm £1,000	
Bridget Farmer	155.	ME – SELF PORTRAIT *Monoprint* N.F.S.	
David Feeley	156.	ANCIENT COLOURS *Oil on canvas* 41 x 41 cm £600	
Jacinta Feeney	157.	TRANSFORMING *Oil on board* 49 x 41 cm £2,500	
Conor Fleck	158.	SELF-PORTRAIT *Charcoal on card* 45 x 36.5 cm £265	
Stephen Forbes	159.	MAGIC FUN *Oil on canvas* 100 x 150 cm £3,400	
Ian Fraser	160.	BABYFACE *Oil on canvas* 30 x 25 cm £750	
Colleen Frew	161.	LANDSCAPE CO. DOWN *Oil on paper* 40 x 48 cm £200	
Ivan Frew	162.	BALLYBOGEY BULL *Etching* 58 x 56 cm £300 £250 u/f	
Victor Gatter	163.	ABORETUM *Pastel* 49 x 73 cm £380	
K. K. Godsee	164.	OPEN VESSEL *Watercolour on handmade paper* 38 x 39 cm £260	
Alan Graham	165.	NEAR SAINTFIELD *Acrylic on canvas* 45 x 45 cm £400	
	166.	SUMMER FIELDS SAINTFIELD *Acrylic* 45 x 45 cm £400	
Sheryl Graham	167.	ORGANIC ARCHITECTURE 1 *Copper on canvas* 122 x 90 cm £550	
Terence Gravett	168.	TIVOLI AU *Screen and woodblock print* 66 x 100 cm £370 u/f £300	
Avril Halliday	169.	THE DAY BEFORE YESTERDAY *Mixed media book* 2 x 13 x 13 cm £300	
	170.	A BACKWARD LOOK *Mixed media book* 3.5 x 13 x 13 cm £300	
Ken Hamilton	171.	STUDY FOR SISTERS *Oil* 15 x 15 cm £ 2,250	
Lynda Hamilton	172.	DO YOU PASS THROUGH? *Screenprint* 48 x 63 cm £250	
Ross Harvey	173.	COASTAL WAVES *Pastel* 81 x 105 cm £1,600	
Carol Henry	174.	RUMINATING *Ceramic* 51 x 18 cm £390	
Ray Henshaw	175.	OCEAN SERIES – BELFAST TO QUEENSTOWN *Screen ink on paper* 70 x 100 cm £550	
	176.	THE WORD *Screen ink on paper* 70 x 100 cm £550	
Rodney Howes	177.	SALMON LEAP, TULLYMORE *Oil* 80 x 78 cm £1,750	
Annabelle Hulbert	178.	THE MARRIAGE VOW *Oil on linen* 53.3 x 48.3 cm £950	
Mark Hutchison	179.	PORTRAIT OF LYNDA *Oil* 20 x 20 cm N.F.S	

Sheila McClean PULSE OF THE BOG

Peter Hutchinson	180.	IMAGINATION ONE *Pen and ink 90 x 60 cm £195*
	181.	IMAGINATION TWO *Pen and ink 70 x 50 cm £156*
Brendan Jamison	182.	SQUASHED TELEPHONE BOX *Bronze 11 x 5 x 5 cm £195*
Alison Jess	183.	TRAFFIC *Pen and ink 59 x 69 cm £1,350*
David Johnston	184.	NUDE STUDY *Oil on canvas 81 x 71 cm £1,100*
Dennis Kelly	185.	THIS IS A HOUSE I NEVER LIVED IN *Enamel on board 750 x 600 cm £1,450*
Josephine Kelly	186.	THE BLUE TREE *Oil on linen 71.1 x 71.1 cm £1,000*
Alick Knox	187.	A NOTION OF A DRAWING *Pencil on paper 32 x 30 cm £320*
	188.	CONSTRUCTION *Pencil on paper 12 x 12 cm £200*
Tomasz Kopera	189.	UNTITLED *Oil 91.4 x 71.1 cm £750*
Mary Kpakra	190.	WHAT LIES BENEATH I *Monotype 63 x 67 cm £295*
Marjorie Leonard	191.	SILVER BIRCH, LOUGH COOLE *Watercolour 67 x 82 cm £650*
	192.	THE WAY THOUGH THE WOODS *Watercolour 84 x 64 cm £750*
Sarah Longley	193.	SELF-PORTRAIT WITH BUTTERFLY CLIP *Oil 59 x 38 cm £1,000*
Padraig MacMiadhachain	194.	THE BLACK HILL THE MULLET, CO MAYO *Oil 44 x 49 cm £895*
Kevin McAleenan	195.	AT ANCHOR *Acrylic 50 x 50 cm £595*
Clement McAleer	196.	FIELD IN TYRONE *Oil on canvas 100 x 10 cm £3,200*
Gavin McCandless	197.	THE ROSSES, DONEGAL *Oil on board 21 x 29 cm £550*
Anna McCaughtry	198.	SURREALIST MACHINE 73 *Bronze mixed media 90 x 90 x 45 cm £750*
Teresa McCoole	199.	ENCOMPASSING OPPOSITES *Beading wire 160 x 160 cm 80 x 80 cm £600*
R. J. McDowell	200.	VESPERS *Oil on canvas 40 x 60 cm £550*
Jill McFarland	201.	UNTITLED 1 *Dyed cotton organdie 240 x 100 cm £500*
	202.	UNTITLED 2 *Dyed cotton organdie 240 x 100 cm £500*
Susan McKeever	203.	EARLY MORNING BELFAST LOUGH *Oil on canvas 92 x 89 cm £950*
Stephen McKeown	204.	ENGLISH BULL TERRIER *Bronze 15 x 28 cm £1,750*
	205.	BULLY *Oil on Board 34 x 29 cm £650*
Kenny McKendry	206.	PRISCILLA AND THE PSYCHIC *Oil on board 61 x 45 cm £2,000*
Maria McKinney	207.	THE SMILE IS RELATIVE *Jigsaw on board 107 x 77 cm £1,950*
Gerard Maguire	208.	SUMMER POOL, DONEGAL *Oil on canvas 40 x 50 cm £850*
Kathryn Marshall	209.	BELFAST CHARMS *Etching 22 x 53 cm £85 Framed £65 uf*
Marie-Louise Martin	210.	MEMENTO *Etching and embossing 54 x 44 cm £350*

Ken Hamilton STUDY FOR SISTERS

Suzanne Martin	211.	DAYS GONE BY *PhotoIntaglio chine colle and drawing 41 x 49 cm £175*
Sam Mateer	212.	TURF BOG, ACHILL *Pastel 80 x 59.5 cm £2,500*
James May	213.	TO HAVE A LITTLE HOUSE *Mixed media 69 x 69 cm £1,875*
	214.	ON A STICK FOR A TREE – OR MAYBE AN APOLOGY, FOR THE GREAT SILENCE *Mixed media 61 x 61 cm £1,625*
James Mercer	215.	THE QUEST *Bronze 51 x 43 cm £1,500*
	216.	3 COUNTIES *Acrylic on board 56 x 70 cm £ 580*
Zoe Murdoch	217.	SOME THINGS ARE BEST KEPT SECRET SOME THINGS ARE BEST KEPT LOST *Mixed 32 x 54.5 x 12 cm £450*
Trudie Mooney	218.	SIX OBJECTS AND A CLOTH *Oil on board 25 x 50 cm £1,500*
	219.	THREE APPLES AND A JUG *Oil on board 23 x 18 cm £ 500*
George Morrow	220.	JANUARY CLOUDS *Oil on board 200 x 255 cm £400*
Hamish Moyle	221.	SOW THISTLES II *Oil on panel 61 x 81 cm £1,500*
Grace Murdock	222.	THE EGG MAN *Oil on paper 50 x 50 cm £200*
Gerry Murphy	223.	THE HAIGHT ASHBURY *Digital print (layered) 95 x 45 cm £225*
Peter Neill	224.	LOOKING FOR PERFECTION *Digital print 55 x 40 cm £250*
	225.	NOT MY LUCKY DAY *Digital print 55 x 40 cm £250*
Elizabeth O'Kane	226.	DAYDREAMER *Bronze 2/10 70 x 25 x 18 cm £3,750*
Rachel O'Neill	227.	LAVA FALL *Dyed velcro polystyrene 200 x 60 x 60 cm £450*
	228.	FROSTED LAVA *Dyed velcro 60 x 80 cm £250*
Red O'Neill	229.	CLASSIC POSE *Mezzotint print 15 x 10 cm £100*
Katherine Penney	230.	SANCTIFY *Photograph 68 x 50 cm £135*
David B. Pettigrew	231.	JOHN GRAY PORTRAIT *Bronzed resin 45.7 x 20.3 x 25.4 cm £8,000*
	232.	MISS AHOGHILL *Bronze 30.2 x 7.6 x 10.2 cm £1,200*
Harry Pettis	233.	DANCE FORM 3 *Inkjet print on photo-rag 30 x 38 cm £125*
Cupar Pilson	234.	SUNDAY MORNING EARLY *Acrylic on board 20 x 43 cm £375*
Padraic Reaney	235.	BOAT PEOPLE *Bronze 26 x 46 cm £1,500*
	236.	THE FAMILY *Bronze 30 x 14 cm £1,200*
Gail Ritchie	237.	MEASURED *Aquarelle and wash on paper 70 x 50 cm £475*
Nicola Robinson	238.	SOUTH PARADE *Oil on canvas 35 x 40 cm £425*
Elizabeth Ruddock	239.	UNDERSTATED VIEW *Irish linen, dyed silk/organza 180 x 180 cm £800*

Jack Pakenham   CLOWN'S HOLIDAY DILEMMA II

Frances Ryan	240.	QUEEN'S ISLAND SERIES NO 1 *Oil on canvas* 122 x 122 cm £3,000
Tim Shaw	241.	HORSE AND CHAINMAIL *Bronze and copperwire ed 8* 22 x 27 x 14 cm £4,900
	242.	BULL GORING HORSE *Bronze ed. 8* 20 x 35 x 15 cm £4,900
John Sherlock	243.	JOHN HUME PORTRAIT BUST *Bronze* 57 x 26 x 22 cm N.F.S
Audrey Smyth	244.	THE GARMENT *Horse hair charcoal on paper* 97 x 66 cm £950
Michael Smyth	245.	NUDE GETTING READY *Oil on board* 76 x 51 cm £1,975
Anushiya Sundaralingam	246.	JOURNEY *Mixed media and wax* 100 x 100 cm £750
Belinda Swingler	247.	MORNING BREEZE *Bronze (unique)* 11.5 x 23.5 x 19 cm £600
Sarah Symes	248.	FUNGAL TRACES *Embossed etching* 20 x 29 cm £130
Emma Teague	249.	TWO-FACED 2 (PINK & PURPLE) *Textile/embroidery* 400 x 150 cm £390
	250.	HOOPLA *Textiles* 400 x 180 cm £450
Elaine Turley	251.	WHY DO WE BUY? *Porcelain slip* 61 x 35.5 cm £500, each pair £250
Peter B. Waddell	252.	SURFACE WATER *Oil on paper* 48 x 64 cm £750
	253.	ACHILL *Oil on paper* 53 x 68 cm £750
Louise Wallace	254.	WHISPER IT TO ME *Oil on canvas* 120 x 60 cm £1,200
Pamela Watson	255.	CONVERSATION 1 *Ceramics, paper, wire, oxides* 55 x 42 x 42 cm £375
	256.	CONVERSATION 2 *Ceramics, paper, wire, oxides* 55 x 50 x 50 cm £400
Raymond Watson	257.	THE LEGEND *Photo etched print* 75 x 60 cm £450 f £350 u/f
	258.	THE COLD FLOOR *Yew* 12 x 45 x 35 cm £1,500
Claire Whitten	259.	ORMEAU AVENUE *Oil on linen* 105 x 85 cm £695
Keith Wilson	260.	LOOKING BACK *Oil on linen* 91.5 x 101.5 cm £4,900
Paul Yates	261.	BEACH SNOWHEAD *Acrylic* 52.5 x 42.5 cm £1,800

A D J U D I C A T O R   A N D   G U E S T   E X H I B I T O R

Pauline Bewick	262.	WOMAN FISHING AT LIKEEN *Watercolour and gold leaf on handmade paper* 98 x 131 cm £14,000
	263.	REACHING FOR ALDER BRANCHES *Watercolour on handmade paper* 98 x 131 cm £12,500

G U E S T   E X H I B I T O R

Hughie O'Donoghue	264.	EXODUS *Oil & Mixed Media on panel* 48.3 x 96.5 cm £8,000

Nicola Robinson SOUTH PARADE

Margaret Arthur MASKED

Anne M. Anderson MAY MORNING

Paul Walls   THERE'S NO PLACE LIKE HOME

Helen Kerr FLYING NORTH

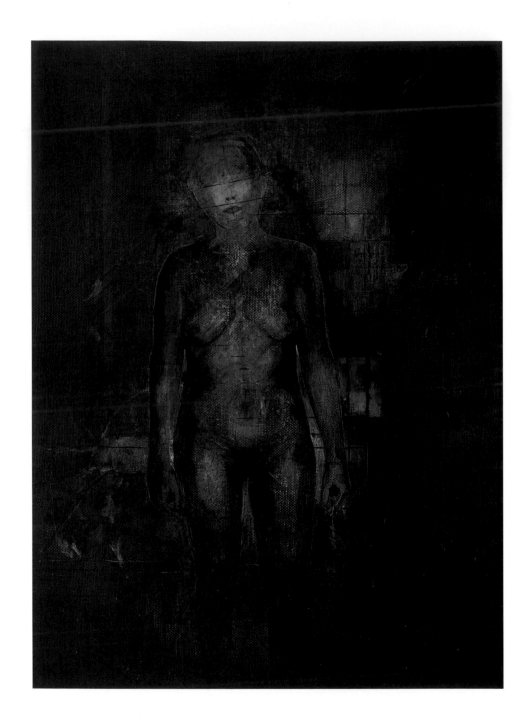

Graham Gingles   NUDE WITH PALM TREE

Rachael Campbell-Palmer DRESS (detail)

Tim Shaw HORSE WITH CHAIN MAIL

Graham Catney TITANIC

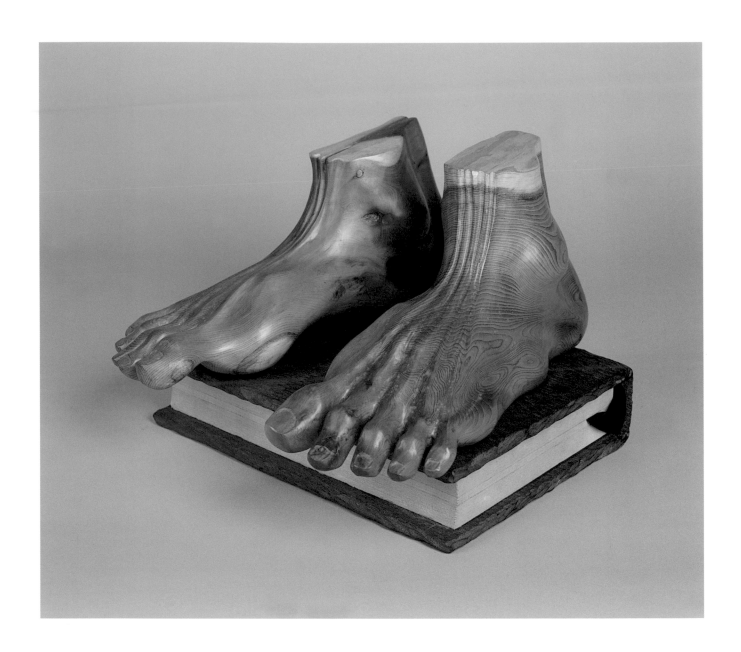

Raymond Watson THE COLD FLOOR

Ross Wilson LEPUS THREE

Fionnuala D'Arcy LANDSCAPE WITH TREES

James May ON A STICK FOR A TREE – OR MAYBE AN APOLOGY, FOR THE GREAT SILENCE

Louise Wallace   WHISPER IT TO ME

Josephine Kelly   THE BLUE TREE

Joanna Mules REANISSANCE

Chris Dearden CHICKEN RUN

Marcus Patton SONGS MY MOTHER TAUGHT ME

Raymond Piper STUDY OF A MALAYSIAN GIRL

Neil Shawcross PORTRAIT OF TED HICKEY

Robert Bottom TOWARDS FAIR HEAD, BALLYCASTLE, CO. ANTRIM

Stephen Dillon   UNTITLED I

Bob Sloan HITCHCOCK'S CHAIR

Gordon McKnight STILL WATERS RUN DEEP IN DONEGAL

Marion Anderson MOORISH PALACE, GRANADA I

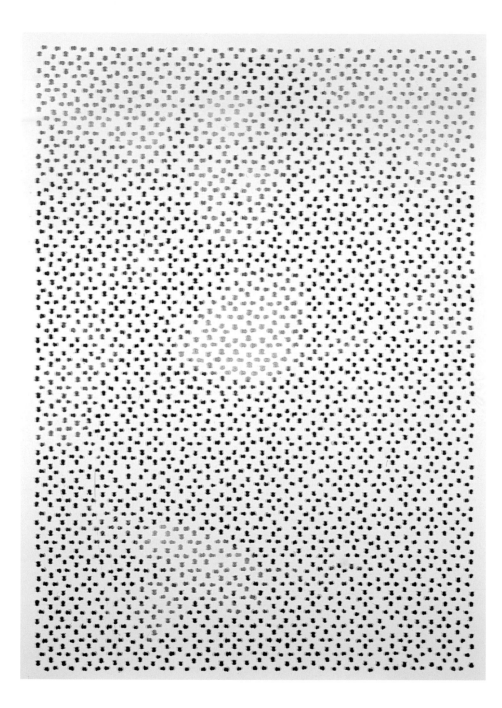

Maria McKinney   THE SMILE IS RELATIVE

Victor Sloan GROUND III

Gail Ritchie MEASURED

Keith Wilson LOOKING BACK

James Allen FIGURES IN AN OLD LANDSCAPE

Trudie Mooney THREE APPLES AND A JUG

Natalia Black PORTAFERRY

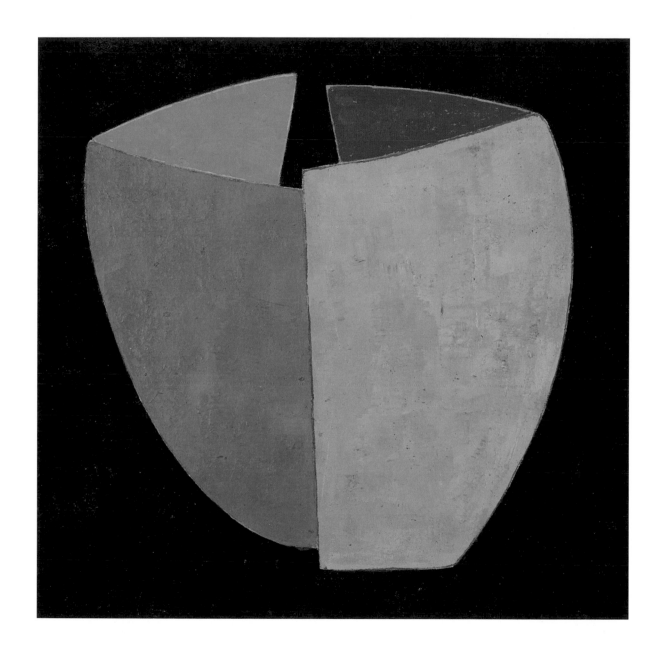

K. K. Godsee OPEN VESSEL

RUA Tel: 07725316583
RUA Website: ruaonline.com